Spooky Manor

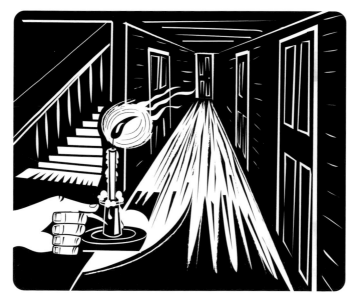

Written by David Orme
Illustrated by Oliver Lake

Titles in Full Flight 5

Badger Publishing Limited
15 Wedgwood Gate, Pin Green Industrial Estate,
Stevenage, Hertfordshire SG1 4SU
Telephone: 01438 356907. Fax: 01438 747015
www.badger-publishing.co.uk
enquiries@badger-publishing.co.uk

Spook Manor   ISBN 978 1 84691 119 4

Series Editor: Jonny Zucker
Publisher: David Jamieson
Commissioning Editor: Carrie Lewis
Editor: Paul Martin
Design: Fiona Grant
Illustration: Oliver Lake

Printed in China through Colorcraft Ltd., Hong Kong

Spook Manor

How to use this book

In this book, YOU are the hero.
DO NOT read through from page to page!

You must choose your own route - but choose wisely or you will face great danger!

Turn over this page to begin.

Follow the 'Go to' prompts when you have chosen your route.

Good luck!

No one can live for long in Spook Manor. Many people have tried, but most of them ended up crazy, or dead – and I mean really, really dead!

But somewhere hidden in Spook Manor there is a great treasure, an ancient painting worth millions! Who is brave enough to search for it?

One evening you are walking past Spook Manor. You see a key lying on the ground – the key to the front door. Here it is:

Are you brave enough to go in and look for the treasure?

No thanks? Well, give this book to someone else who *is* brave enough and go and read something less scary instead.

Yes, you're up for it? I thought so!
Go to 1

1 You approach the big front door. There are two keyholes but only one will work. Which keyhole will you try? Check your key carefully!

Keyhole 13? **Go to 13**
Keyhole 36? **Go to 36**

→2 You scramble along the tunnel. At last you reach the inside of a well. A ladder goes upwards and downwards.

Which way will you climb?
Upwards? **Go to 20**
Downwards? **Go to 29**

→3 You are in the blue bedroom. All is quiet here. There is a cupboard in the corner and a door in one of the walls.

Will you…
Open the cupboard? **Go to 10**
Go through the door? **Go to 16**
Leave the room? **Go to 9**

→4 Just in time, you leap out of the window. But you have left the key to the house inside on the floor of the dining room – with the rats! **Go to 44**

➡5 Didn't I tell you that the valuable painting was an ancient one? How can an ancient picture show a space ship?

The picture is a time transporter. By mistake, you press a hidden switch. The next thing you know you have travelled into the future. You find that you are now the skeleton. You sit down in the armchair and reach for the paper.

Sadly, there is no return...
Go to 40

➡6 Well done – you have solved the riddle! Leave the bathroom quickly before the riddle genie thinks of another one. **Go to 9**

→**7** You are in the cellar. You hold up your candle and see… a coffin! Beyond it, some junk is piled up against the wall.

Nearby, there are two doors, one green and one brown. A flight of stairs heads up to the hall. Inside the coffin is a vampire, Count Rack-o-Ribs. You know that you are safe for now as vampires only come out when it is dark.

Just then, a bat flies into you and knocks the candle from your hand. In the darkness, you hear the coffin opening…

What are you going to do?
Rush up the stairs to the main hall?
Go to 39
Try the brown door? **Go to 28**
Try the green door? **Go to 34**

➤8 You scramble along the tunnel and find yourself in the cellar.
Go to 12

➤9 You are on the first floor landing. There are three bedroom doors painted different colours, a bathroom door and a small rickety flight of stairs leading up to the attic.

Choose carefully!
The red door? **Go to 16**
The blue door? **Go to 3**
The purple door? **Go to 30**
The bathroom? **Go to 14**
Go up to the attic? **Go to 18**
Go down the stairs to the hall? **Go to 19**

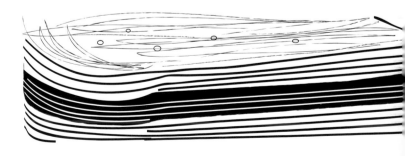

➜ **10** The cupboard is dark. You step inside and find yourself falling... until you land on a pile of old mattresses. Luckily, you are not injured, but you have lost the key to the front door. You are in a shed leaning against the wall of the house. Go outside. **Go to 20**

➡ **11** You spend all night looking through the boxes, but you don't find any more paintings.

In the morning, you start to go down the stairs, but a huge and deadly spider has built a web across the top of the stairs. You are trapped in the attic!

You look through the keyhole of the door in the corner and see a spiral staircase going down. You manage to smash the lock with a piece of junk and head down the stairs, passing two locked doors on the way down.

Finally, you go through a green door into the cellar. In the middle of the room is a coffin – inside is the vampire, Count Rack-o-Ribs. Luckily, it is now morning, so he is fast asleep. You realise to your horror that you have left the picture of the castle in the attic!

You turn to go back up the spiral stairs, but the green door is now stuck and you can't smash it open.

What do you do?
Go up the stairs to the hall? **Go to 41**
Explore the cellar? **Go to 24**

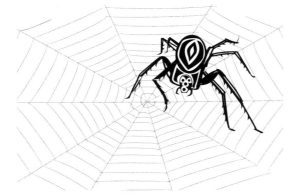

➜12 You have had to push something aside to get into the cellar. It is a painting showing a saint. Luckily, it is quite small, so you can put it inside your rucksack.

What will you do now?
Explore the cellar? **Go to 7**
Go back to the well? **Go to 2**

➔ 13 Oops! Wrong keyhole. The key breaks in the lock. The door won't open. You will have to try again from the start if you want to find the painting.
Go back to 1

➔ 14 You are in the bathroom. A powerful riddle genie lives here, in a bottle of shampoo. He ties you up and drops you in the bath. He turns the water on. Unless you can solve his riddle, you are going to drown!

My first letter's in spook, but not in pool,
My second's in in, and it, that's the rule,
My last's like a cross and, unless you're a fool,
You've solved it! Yes, riddles are scarily cool!

If you've worked out the answer, go to it! If you haven't, **go to 40**.

→15 You climb down the well. Luckily, you had a spare candle in your pocket and you hold it between your teeth. You find a slimy wet tunnel in the wall of the well. What are you going to do?

Explore the tunnel? **Go to 8**
Carry on down? **Go to 29**

➔16 You are in the red bedroom. In the middle of the room is a four-poster bed with curtains all round it. In one of the walls is a door.

What's the plan?
Investigate the bed? **Go to 23**
Try the door? **Go to 3**

➔17 You are in the dining room. The last people to live in the house left a meal on the table and now the room is full of hungry rats. They have eaten all the food and now they are going to eat *you*…

What do you do?
Rush back into the entrance hall?
Go to 22
Grab a heavy chair, smash the window with it and jump out? **Go to 4**

➡ **18** You are in the attic. In the corner is a doorway that won't open. The attic is stuffed with old boxes and heaps of junk. The first box you open has an old painting showing a ruined castle.

What will you do now?
Go downstairs with the painting?
Go to 9
Carry on looking through the boxes and junk? **Go to 11**

19 A green ghoul called Gerald is sitting on the stairs. You can't go this way! **Go back to 9**

20 You find you are in a garden. A gate leads onto the road.

Do you want to escape from the house?
Go to 44
There is a well in the garden with a ladder going down it. Give it a try?
Go to 15

21 You are in the study. The door shuts behind you with a slam. You're locked in. You try breaking the windows, but they seem super strong. There is a big fireplace in the wall. You try to escape this way. **Go to 38**

22 The door has locked itself! The rats are really, really hungry...
Go to 40

➡ **23** You pull aside the curtains. The ghost of Sir Reginald Piffle is waiting behind the curtain. Luckily, he is friendly!

You ask Sir Reginald where the valuable painting is, but he can't talk. He points downwards with his finger…

Go through the door to 3.

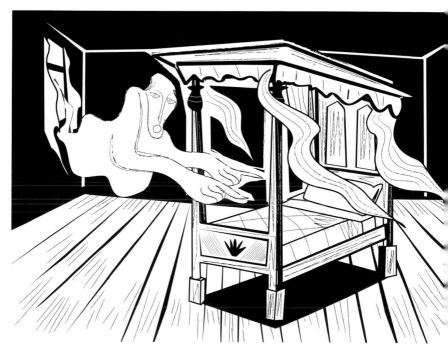

➡24 There is a pile of dusty junk in the corner of the cellar. You pull it away and find a painting of a saint leaning against the wall.

Luckily, the painting is quite small, so you put it in your rucksack.

Also behind the junk, there is a tunnel. You enter the tunnel – it's your only chance! **Go to 2**

➡25 You are in the sitting room. In one corner, a skeleton is sitting in an armchair reading the newspaper. On the wall is a picture of a space ship.

What do you do?
Leave the picture where it is and go back into the hall? **Go to 37**
Take the picture off the wall? **Go to 5**

➜**26** You go out into the yard and the kitchen door slams shut behind you. You can't get back in – and you left the key to the front door in the kitchen. A path leads you round to the front of the house, and the road.

Your adventure is over… **Go to 44**

➜**27** This painting is by the famous painter, Leonardo da Luton. You are rich! Congratulations! You have won the challenge and can live a life of luxury.

THE END

➜28 Oh dear! This is just a cupboard. There is no escape! Count Rack-o-Ribs has got you! You feel his teeth sinking into your neck…
Go to 40

➜29 The ladder here is rotten. There is a crack and you find you are falling, falling… into very deep water. **Go to 40**

➜30 You are in a purple bedroom. In the corner of the room, there is a doorway leading to a spiral staircase which goes up and down.

Where will you go?
Up the spiral stairs? **Go to 45**
Down the spiral stairs and open the door at the bottom? **Go to 7**
Go through the bedroom door? **Go to 9**

➜31 Stopping the tap dripping was a mistake. Desmond the house demon lives under the sink and the dripping kept him asleep.

After a struggle, Desmond locks you in the cupboard under the sink. He has started the tap dripping. Drip, drip, drip – on and on for hours. You can't stand it any more…
Go to 40

➔32 Something has sealed the door! You cannot get out this way. **Go back to 37**

➔33 You have got the wrong one! This picture is a fake – it's not worth anything! But at least you are alive...

THE END

Why not go back to 1 and try again?

➔34 You open the door and find a spiral staircase leading upwards, so you start climbing quickly. You go through the first door you can open. **Go to 30**

➔35 This was a big mistake. The chimney gets narrower and narrower. At last you are stuck and you can't go up or down. In fifty years time, your skeleton will be found when the house is knocked down. **Go to 40**

➜36 The door creaks open and a flock of bats flies past you into the gloomy evening.

You are inside the front hall of Spook Manor. You find some candles and matches in a cupboard. You light one and look around. **Go to 37**

➜**37** A wide flight of stairs goes up to the first floor. Five doors open onto the hall. Which one will you open?

Dining room? **Go to 17**
Sitting room? **Go to 25**
Study? **Go to 21**
Kitchen? **Go to 42**
Door to the cellar? **Go to 7**
Climb the stairs? **Go to 9**
Go back out of the front door? **Go to 32**

➜**38** You climb up the sooty chimney. At last, you reach a place where another chimney joins.

You could:
Carry on upwards? **Go to 35**
Go down the chimney that has joined on? **Go to 25**

➜**39** You rush to the stairs, but trip over the bottom step and fall to the ground. Count Rack-o-Ribs has got you! You feel his teeth sinking into your neck…
Go to 40

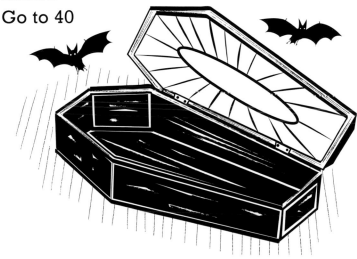

➜40 Looks like you've met a terrible fate inside Spook Manor. Don't say we didn't warn you!

THE END
Return to 1 to have another try.

➜ 41 Sorry, you can't open the cellar door from inside. You'll just have to explore the cellar and hope there is another way out – or wait until Count Rack-o-Ribs wakes up! **Go to 24**

➜ **42** You are in the kitchen. There is a door leading out to a yard. In the corner, there is another door. You peep through the keyhole and see that there is a spiral staircase behind it, going up and down, but the door is locked. The tap is dripping – drip, drip, drip – someone has been trying water torture!

What are you going to do?
Go out into the yard? **Go to 26**
Go back into the hall? **Go to 37**
Stop the tap dripping? **Go to 31**

➜ **43** Do you have...
The picture of the castle? **Go to 33**
The picture of the saint? **Go to 27**

➔44 You reach the road, and you are alive! But have you found any pictures?

Yes? **Go to 43**

No? Then you are leaving empty handed. Your quest has failed. If you would like to try again, **go to 1.**

➔45 You try walking up the stairs, but the way is blocked by a locked door. **Go back to 30**

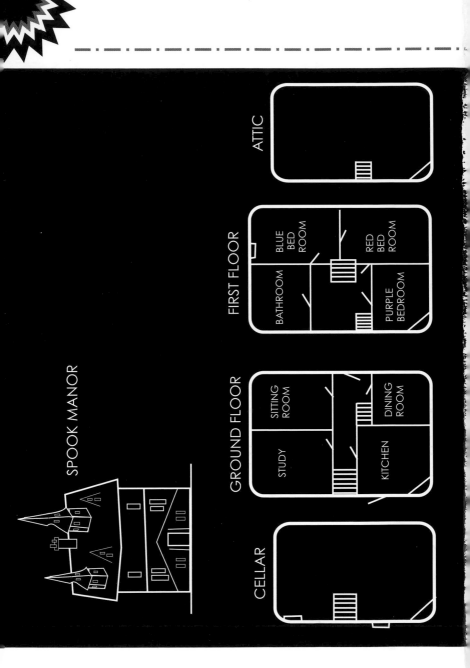

SPOOK MANOR

ATTIC

FIRST FLOOR

BLUE BED ROOM

RED BED ROOM

BATHROOM

PURPLE BEDROOM

GROUND FLOOR

SITTING ROOM

STUDY

DINING ROOM

KITCHEN

CELLAR